The echidna and the shade tree

Told by
Mona Green
Retold and illustrated by
Pamela Lofts

ASHTON SCHOLASTIC
SYDNEY AUCKLAND NEW YORK TORONTO LONDON

Away out in the middle of the desert,
there once grew a huge tree.

It was so big, that it shaded
the whole land
from the scorching sun.

All the animals lived in the shade of this tree.
Each day, they would hunt for food,
while old Echidna stayed behind.
He looked after the children.

Each time, when the animals returned with the food,
they would give the children the tastiest bits –

but poor old Echidna got only the scraps.

This made Echidna very angry!
He grabbed hold of that giant shade tree
and shook it.
He pulled it.
And, with a mighty tug, tore it right
out of the ground – roots and all.

He put the tree on his back and stomped off.

Soon, the animals realised that their shade was moving
and that they would die of thirst in the hot sun.

They chased after Echidna
and begged him to stop.
They begged him to put
the tree back.

But he just marched on in anger.

The animals threw a boomerang.
Surely that would stop him!

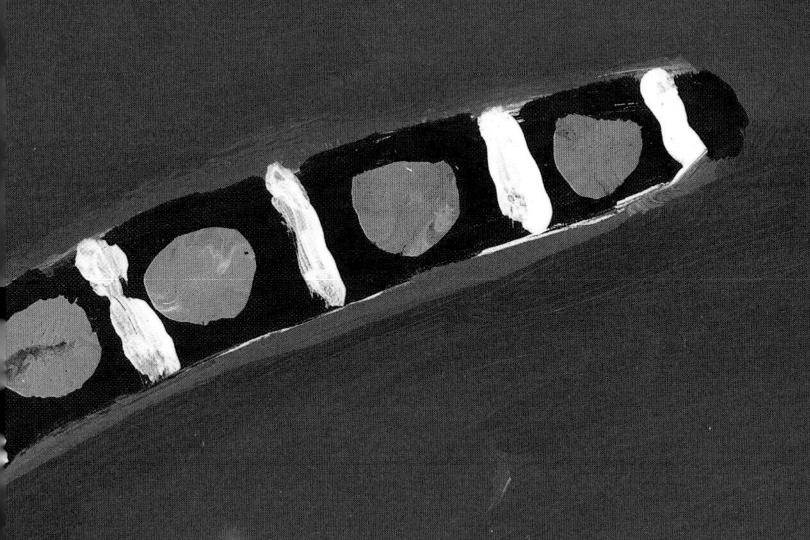

But it didn't.
It hit him on the feet and broke his toes –

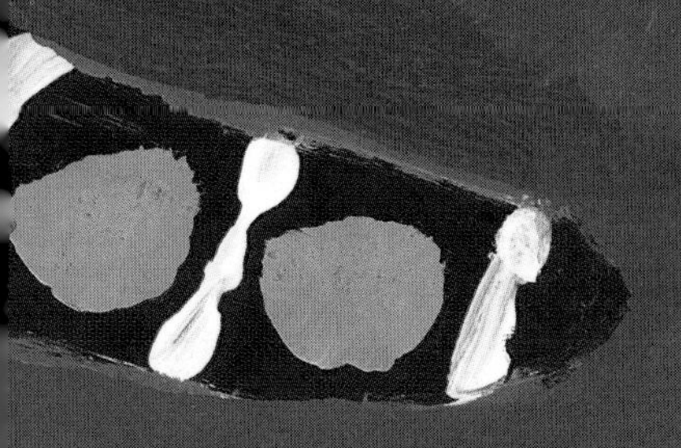

But he still shuffled on!

At last, the animals hurled their spears.

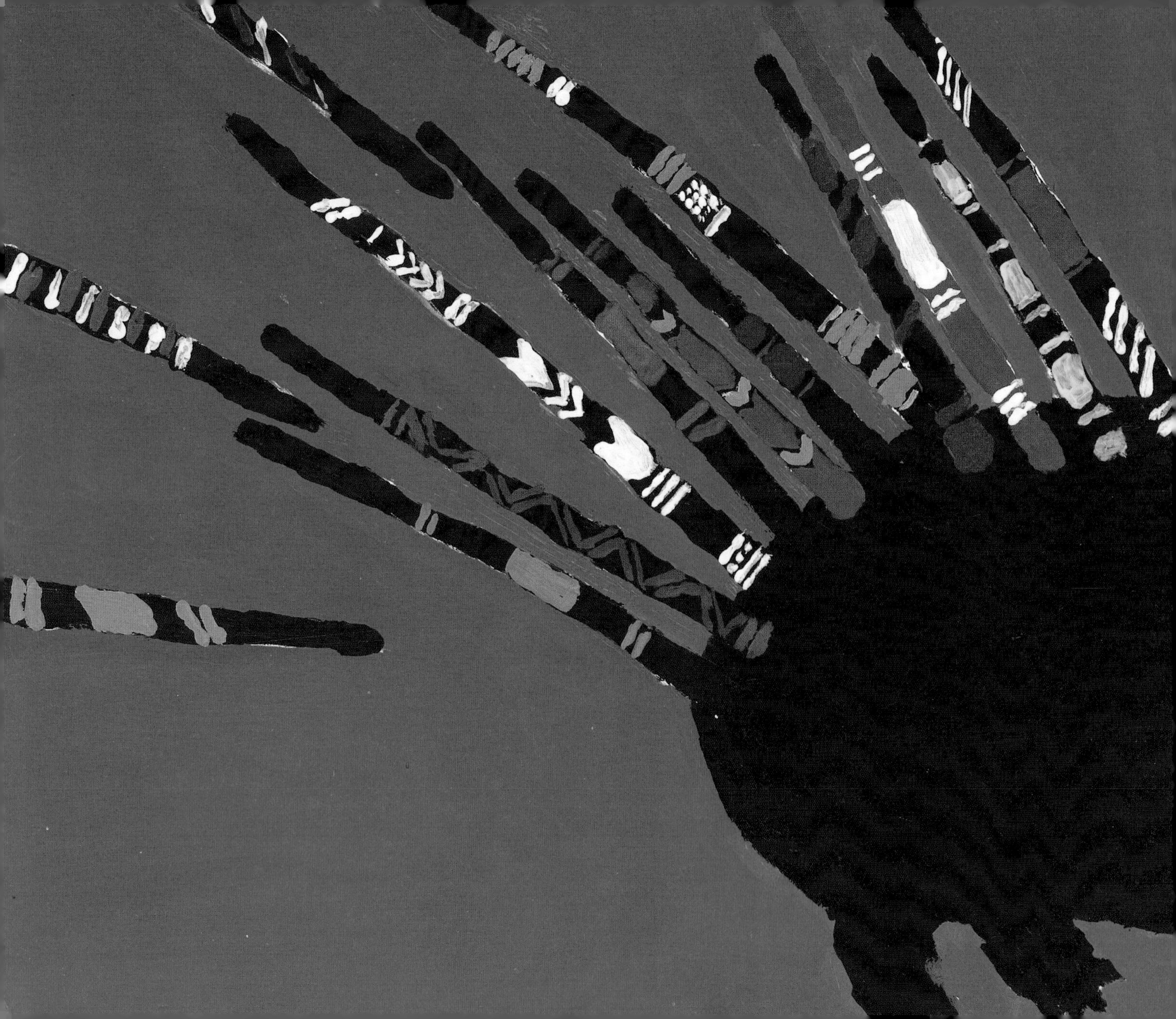

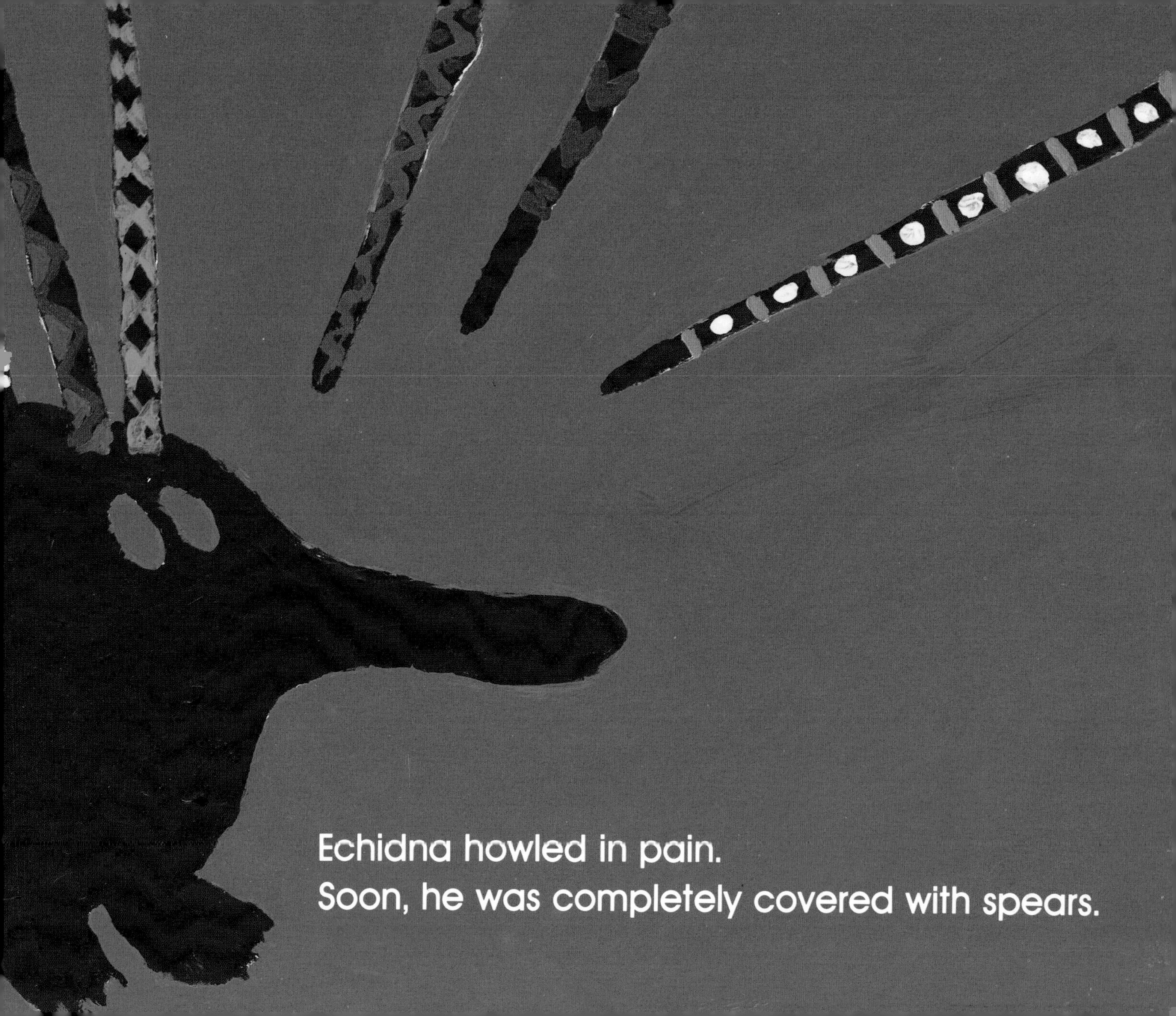

Echidna howled in pain.
Soon, he was completely covered with spears.

The giant tree crashed to the ground.
It rolled over and over
across the plain –

and its huge branches
broke off and
stuck into the ground.

Poor Echidna lay dying.
Soon the animals began to feel sorry for him.

Cockatoo flew up and asked,
'Where would you like to be buried?

In an antbed?

In a clump of spinifex grass?
In between some rocks?'

Echidna chose the rocks.
When he died, the animals buried him there
and covered him up.
Only the spears were sticking out.

To this day, echidnas have spears
on their backs.
They still shuffle about on
little bent and broken feet,
as they hunt for ants amongst the rocks.

The animals, too, still live in the desert.
They hunt in the shade of
the small trees that grew
from the branches of
that one giant tree.

And they will never die of thirst,
because water filled up the hole left by
the shade tree – and made a huge lake,
called Nongra.